Victoriana

KEEPSAKE

A

Name	*Name* ....
Tel	*Tel* ....
Address	*Address* ....
....	....
....	....
....	....

Name	*Name* ....
Tel	*Tel* ....
Address	*Address* ....
....	....
....	....
....	....

Name	*Name* ....
Tel	*Tel* ....
Address	*Address* ....
....	....
....	....
....	....

Notes & Numbers

Personal Notes

Name ....

Address ....

....

....

Telephone ....

....

In Case of Emergency

Contact ....

Tel No. ....

Blood Group ....

Allergies ....

Useful Information (Passport Details, Car Info etc.)

....

....

....

Dates to Remember

Date   Event

A-B

Name ....
Tel ....
Address ....
....
....
....

Name ....
Tel ....
Address ....
....
....
....

Name ....
Tel ....
Address ....
....
....
....

Name ....
Tel ....
Address ....
....
....
....

Name ....
Tel ....
Address ....
....
....

Name ....
Tel ....
Address ....
....
....

B

Name ....
Tel ....
Address ....
....
....

Name ....
Tel ....
Address ....
....
....

Name ....
Tel ....
Address ....
....

B

Name ....
Tel ....
Address ....
....
....

Name ....
Tel ....
Address ....
....
....

Name ....
Tel ....
Address ....
....

C

Name ....

Tel ....

Address ....

....

....

....

Name ....

Tel ....

Address ....

....

....

....

Name ....

Tel ....

Address ....

....

....

....

Name ....

Tel ....

Address ....

....

....

....

Name ....

Tel ....

Address ....

....

....

....

Name ....

Tel ....

Address ....

....

....

....

Sincerity

Quotations for Special Occasions

"You will find as you look back
upon your life that the moments
when you have really lived are the
moments when you have done
things in the spirit of love."

Henry Drummond

"God gave us memories that we
might have roses in December."

James M. Barrie

"The worse the passage
the more welcome the port."

Thomas Fuller

"Knowledge may give weight,
but accomplishments give lustre,
and many more people see
than weigh."

Lord Chesterfield

"Parting is all we know of heaven
And all we need of hell."

Emily Dickinson

"Don't let what you cannot do
interfere with what you can do."

John Wooden

"Life is either a daring adventure
or nothing. To keep our faces
toward change and behave like
free spirits in the presence of fate
is strength undefeatable."

Helen Keller

"Life is cut to allow for growth
. . . one may vigorously put
on weight before one fills
it out entirely."

Rainer Maria Rilke

Quotations for Special Occasions

"Only two things are necessary
to keep one's wife happy.
One is to let her think she is
having her own way, and the other,
to let her have it."

Lyndon B. Johnson

"Every baby born into the world
is a finer one than the last."

Charles Dickens: Nicholas Nickleby

"He conquers who endures."

Italian Proverb

"The greater the obstacle, the
more glory we have in overcoming
it; the difficulties with which we
are met are the maids of honour
which set off virtue."

Molière

"Our duty is to be useful,
not according to our desires,
but according to our powers."

Henri Frédérick Amiel

"Education is what survives
when what has been learnt
has been forgotten."

B. F. Skinner

"Our youth we can have
but to-day,
We may always find time
to grow old."

George Berkeley

"You see things and you say,
'Why?' But I dream things that
never were; and I say 'Why not?' "

Thomas Edison

C-D

Name ....

Tel ....

Address ....

....

....

....

Name ....

Tel ....

Address ....

....

....

....

Name ....

Tel ....

Address ....

....

....

....

Name ....

Tel ....

Address ....

....

....

....

Name ....

Tel ....

Address ....

....

....

....

Name ....

Tel ....

Address ....

....

....

....

So Teach Us to Number Our Days, That We May Apply Our Hearts Into Wisdom.
Psalm 90.12.

To one I love

Quotations for Special Occasions

"Whatever is worth doing at all is worth doing well."

Lord Chesterfield

"Friendship multiplies the good of life and divides the evil. 'Tis the sole remedy against misfortune, the very ventilation of the soul."

Baltasar Gracian

"I like the dreams of the future better than the history of the past."

Thomas Jefferson

"To be without some of the things you want is an indispensable part of happiness."

Bertrand Russell

"By all means marry; if you have a good wife, you'll become happy; if you have a bad one, you'll become a philosopher."

Socrates

"When I was at home, I was in a better place."

William Shakespeare: As You Like It

"A whole bushel of wheat is made up of single grains."

Thomas Fuller

"He who binds to himself a joy Does the winged life destroy; But he who kisses the joy as it flies Lives in eternity's sunrise."

William Blake: Eternity

Quotations for Special Occasions

"'Tis sweet to know there is
an eye will mark
Our coming, and look brighter
when we come."

Byron: Don Juan

"Learn as though you would never
be able to master it;
hold it as though you would be
in fear of losing it."

Confucius

"To the art of working well a
civilised race would add the art of
playing well."

George Santayana

"Marriage is three parts love and
seven parts forgiveness of sins."

Langdon Mitchell

"Immature love says:
'I love you because I need you.'
Mature love says: 'I need you
because I love you.' "

Erich Fromm

"We have not passed that subtle
line between childhood and
adulthood until we move from
the passive voice to the active
voice – that is, until we have
stopped saying 'It got lost,'
and say, 'I lost it.' "

Sydney J. Harris

"The denunciation of the young is
a necessary part of the hygiene of
older people, and greatly assists
the circulation of the blood."

Logan Pearsall Smith

D

Name	....
Tel	....
Address	....
	....
	....
	....

Name	....
Tel	....
Address	....
	....
	....
	....

Name	....
Tel	....
Address	....
	....
	....
	....

Name	....
Tel	....
Address	....
	....
	....
	....

Name	....
Tel	....
Address	....
	....
	....
	....

Name	....
Tel	....
Address	....
	....
	....
	....

E

Name ....
Tel ....
Address ....
....
....

Name ....
Tel ....
Address ....
....
....

Name ....
Tel ....
Address ....
....
....

E

Name ....
Tel ....
Address ....
....
....

Name ....
Tel ....
Address ....
....
....

Name ....
Tel ....
Address ....
....
....

Quotations for Special Occasions

"How to make a speech:
Be sincere
Be brief
Be seated."

Anon

"A man's real possession is his memory. In nothing else is he rich, in nothing else is he poor."

Alexander Smith

"The secret of success in life is for a man to be ready for his opportunity when it comes."

Benjamin Disraeli

"Mother is the name for God in the lips and hearts of little children."

W. M. Thackeray: Vanity Fair

"Cessation of work is not accompanied by cessation of expenses."

Cato the Elder

"'Tis better to have loved and lost, Than never to have loved at all."

Alfred Lord Tennyson

"We make a living by what we get, but we make a life by what we give."

Norman MacEwan

"To leave is to die a little;
It is to die to what one loves.
One leaves behind
a little of oneself
At any hour, any place."

Edmond Haraucourt

E-F

Name ....
Tel ....
Address ....
....
....
....

Name ....
Tel ....
Address ....
....
....
....

Name ....
Tel ....
Address ....
....
....
....

Name ....
Tel ....
Address ....
....
....
....

Name ....
Tel ....
Address ....
....
....

Name ....
Tel ....
Address ....
....
....

F

Name ....
Tel ....
Address ....
....
....

Name ....
Tel ....
Address ....
....
....

Name ....
Tel ....
Address ....
....
....

F

Name ....
Tel ....
Address ....
....
....

Name ....
Tel ....
Address ....
....
....

Name ....
Tel ....
Address ....
....

Quotations for Special Occasions

"Behold the turtle.
He makes progress only when
he sticks his neck out."

James B. Conant

"Human misery must
somewhere have a stop:
there is no wind that always
blows a storm."

Euripides

"A good natured man has the
whole world to be happy out of."

Alexander Pope

"The world's a scene of changes,
and to be
Constant, in Nature
were inconstancy."

Abraham Cowley

"A baby is an angel whose wings
decrease as his legs increase."

French Proverb

"It needs courage to let our
children go, but we are trustees
and stewards and have to hand
them back to life – to God.
As the old saying puts it:
'What I gave I have.' We have
to love them and lose them."

Alfred Torrie

"An agreeable companion on a
journey is as good as a carriage."

Publilius Syrus

"They can conquer who
believe they can."

John Dryden

Quotations for Special Occasions

"Aim at the sun, and you may not reach it; but your arrow will fly far higher than if aimed at an object on a level with yourself."

J. Hawes

"Oft expectations fails
and most oft there
Where most it promises,
and oft it hits
Where hope is coldest
and despair most fits."

*William Shakespeare:
All's Well that Ends Well*

"The greatest wealth is to
live content with little,
for there is never want where
the mind is satisfied."

Lucretius

"He who has gone, so we but cherish his memory, abides with us, more potent, nay, more present, than the living man."

Saint-Exupéry

"Destiny is not a matter of chance,
it is a matter of choice;
it is not a thing to be waited for,
it is a thing to be achieved."

W. J. Bryan

"Education is an ornament
in prosperity and a refuge
in adversity."

Aristotle

"An ideal wife is any woman
who has an ideal husband."

Booth Tarkington

Quotations for Special Occasions

"When brothers agree,
no fortress is so strong as
their common life."

Antisthenes

"When I'm not thanked at all,
I'm thanked enough,
I've done my duty,
and I've done no more."

Henry Fielding

"Love doesn't sit there like
a stone, it has to be made,
like bread; remade all the time,
made new."

Ursula K. Le Guin

"Problems are opportunities
in work clothes."

Henry Kaiser

"God could not be everywhere,
so He made mothers."

Jewish Proverb

"Weep not that the world changes
– did it keep
A stable, changeless state,
'twere cause indeed to weep."

William Cullen Bryant

"A man's maturity consists
in having found again the
seriousness one had as
a child, at play."

F. W. Nietzsche

"Dismiss the old horse in good
time, lest he fail in the lists and
the spectators laugh."

Horace

To one I love

G

Name ....
Tel ....
Address ....
....
....
....

Name ....
Tel ....
Address ....
....
....
....

Name ....
Tel ....
Address ....
....
....

G

Name ....
Tel ....
Address ....
....
....
....

Name ....
Tel ....
Address ....
....
....
....

Name ....
Tel ....
Address ....
....
....

G-H

Name ....
Tel ....
Address ....
....
....
....

Name ....
Tel ....
Address ....
....
....
....

Name ....
Tel ....
Address ....
....
....
....

Name ....
Tel ....
Address ....
....
....
....

Name ....
Tel ....
Address ....
....
....
....

Name ....
Tel ....
Address ....
....
....
....

H

Name ....
....
....
....
....

Name ....
Tel ....
Address ....
....
....

Name ....
Tel ....
Address ....
....
....

H

Name ....
Tel ....
Address ....
....

Name ....
Tel ....
Address ....
....

Name ....
Tel ....
Address ....
....

Quotations for Special Occasions

"If at first you don't succeed,
Try, try, try again."

William Edward Hickson

"Skill and confidence are
an unconquered army."

George Herbert

"When I was a boy of fourteen,
my father was so ignorant I could
hardly stand to have the old man
around. But when I got to be
twenty one, I was astonished at
how much he had learned in
seven years."

Mark Twain

"To me old age is always fifteen
years older than I am."

Bernard Baruch

"Success generally depends
upon knowing how long
it takes to succeed."

C. L. de Montesquieu

"I enjoy convalescence.
It is the part that makes the
illness worth while."

George Bernard Shaw

"Sorrow is better than fear . . .
Fear is a journey, a terrible journey,
but sorrow is at least
an arriving."

Alan Paton: Cry, The Beloved Country

"All who joy would win
Must share it,—
Happiness was born a Twin."

Byron: Don Juan

Quotations for Special Occasions

"The young man who wants to marry happily should pick out a good mother and marry one of her daughters – any one will do."

J. Ogden Armour

"What is this life if, full of care, We have no time to stand and stare?"

W. H. Davies

"It isn't how long you stick around but what you put over while you are here."

George Ade

"Of cheerfulness, or a good temper – the more it is spent, the more of it remains."

Ralph Waldo Emerson

"Our hours in love have wings; in absence crutches."

Colley Cibber

"He knows not his own strength that hath not met adversity."

Ben Jonson

"It is better to waste one's youth than to do nothing with it at all."

Georges Courtline

"Through loyalty to the past, our mind refuses to realise that tomorrow's joy is possible only if today's makes way for it; that each wave owes the beauty of its line only to the withdrawal of the preceding one."

André Gide

I

Name ....   Name ....
Tel ....   Tel ....
Address ....   Address ....
....
....
....

Name ....   Name ....
Tel ....   Tel ....
Address ....   Address ....
....
....
....

Name ....   Name ....
Tel ....   Tel ....
Address ....   Address ....
....
....

His
Compass
fail
They are n
every
morning.

Quotations for Special Occasions

"Don't be afraid to take big steps.
You can't cross a chasm in
two small jumps."

David Lloyd George

"It is always darkest just before
the day dawneth."

Thomas Fuller

"To die completely, a person must
not only forget but be forgotten,
and he who is not forgotten
is not dead."

Samuel Butler

"There's nothing worth
the wear of winning,
But laughter and the love
of friends."

Hilaire Belloc

"Memory is the diary that we
all carry about with us."

Oscar Wilde

"There are difficulties in your
path. Be thankful for them.
They will test your capabilities of
resistance; you will be impelled
to persevere from the very
energy of the opposition.
But what of him that fails?
What does he gain?
Strength for life. The real merit is
not in the success, but in the
endeavour; and win or lose,
he will be honoured and crowned."

W. Punshon

"The shortest answer is doing."

George Herbert

I-J

Name ....
Tel ....
Address ....
....
....
....

Name ....
Tel ....
Address ....
....
....
....

Name ....
Tel ....
Address ....
....
....
....

Name ....
Tel ....
Address ....
....
....
....

Name ....
Tel ....
Address ....
....
....
....

Name ....
Tel ....
Address ....
....
....
....

Quotations for Special Occasions

"All love is sweet,
Given or returned.
Common as light is love,
And its familiar voice
wearies not ever."

Shelley: Prometheus Unbound

"You must never 'find' time
for anything. If you want time
you must make it."

Charles Buxton

"Whoever, in middle age,
attempts to realise the wishes
and hope of his early youth,
invariably deceives himself.
Each ten years of a man's life has
its own fortunes, its own hopes,
its own desires."

Johann Wolfgang von Goethe

"They will say that you are on the
wrong road, if it is your own."

Antonio Porchia

"There is no more lovely, friendly
and charming relationship,
communion or company than a
good marriage."

Martin Luther

"Originality does not consist in
saying what no one has ever said
before, but in saying exactly what
you think yourself."

James Fitz-James Stephen

"Growing old is no more than a
bad habit which a busy man has
no time to form."

André Maurois

J

Name ....
Tel ....
Address ....
....
....
....

Name ....
Tel ....
Address ....
....
....
....

Name ....
Tel ....
Address ....
....
....
....

Name ....
Tel ....
Address ....
....
....
....

Name ....
Tel ....
Address ....
....
....
....

Name ....
Tel ....
Address ....
....
....
....

Quotations for Special Occasions

"The magic of first love is our ignorance that it can ever end."

Benjamin Disraeli

"There is no home that is not twice as beautiful as the most beautiful city."

West African Proverb

"A man's growth is seen in the successive choirs of his friends."

Ralph Waldo Emerson

"Nothing speaks our grief so well As to speak nothing."

Richard Crashaw

"A true friend is the greatest of all blessings."

François de la Rochefoucauld

"Marriage is not a finished affair. No matter to what age you live, love must be continuously consolidated. Being considerate, thoughtful and respectful without ulterior motives is the key to a successful marriage."

Pamphlet from Chinese Family Planning Centre

"A man of learning has riches within him."

Phaedrus: Fabulae Æsopiae

"Experience shows that success is due less to ability than to zeal. The winner is he who gives himself to his work, body and soul."

Charles Buxton

K

Name ....
Tel ....
Address ....
....
....
....

Name ....
Tel ....
Address ....
....
....
....

Name ....
Tel ....
Address ....
....
....

K

Name ....
Tel ....
Address ....
....
....
....

Name ....
Tel ....
Address ....
....
....
....

Name ....
Tel ....
Address ....
....
....

Quotations for Special Occasions

"It matters not how long you live,
but how well."

Publilius Syrus

"Womanliness means only
motherhood;
All love begins and ends there."

Robert Browning

"The man who wins may have
been counted out several times,
but he didn't hear the referee."

H. E. Jansen

"What is the odds so long as
the fire of soul is kindled at the
taper of conviviality, and the
wing of friendship never
moults a feather?"

Charles Dickens

"An investment in knowledge
always pays the best interest."

Benjamin Franklin

"One word
Frees us of all the weight
and pain of life:
That word is love."

Sophocles

"Though all men be made
of one metal, yet they be
not cast all in one mould."

John Lyly: Euphues

"Honour and shame
from no condition rise;
Act well your part:
there all the honour lies."

Alexander Pope

K

Name ....
Tel ....
Address ....
....
....
....

Name ....
Tel ....
Address ....
....
....
....

Name ....
Tel ....
Address ....
....
....
....

L

Name ....
Tel ....
Address ....
....
....
....

Name ....
Tel ....
Address ....
....
....
....

Name ....
Tel ....
Address ....
....
....
....

For the sunshine
and the rain.
For the dew and for
the shower.
For the yellow
ripened ...
And the golden
harvest ...
... bless ...
O ...

... God
is a sun and shield:
the Lord will give
Grace and Glory:
... no good thing
will He withhold
... them that
walk uprightly.

Quotations for Special Occasions

"Sunset and evening star,
And one clear call for me!
And may there be no moaning
of the bar,
When I put out to sea."

Alfred Lord Tennyson

"Our strength often increases in
proportion to the obstacles
imposed upon it."

Paul de Rapin

"Marriage is like life in this –
that it is a field of battle,
and not a bed of roses."

Robert Louis Stevenson

"By asking for the impossible
we obtain the best possible."

Italian Proverb

"Years ago we discovered the exact
point, the dead centre of middle
age. It occurs when you are too
young to take up golf and too old
to rush up to the net."

Franklin P. Adams

"The only cure for grief is action."

G. H. Lewes

"Whatever is formed for long
duration arrives slowly to its
maturity."

Samuel Johnson (on ageing)

"Silence is the perfectest herald
of joy. I were but little happy if
I could say how much."

*William Shakespeare:
Much Ado About Nothing*

L

Name ....
Tel ....
Address ....
....
....
....

Name ....
Tel ....
Address ....
....
....
....

Name ....
Tel ....
Address ....
....
....

Name ....
Tel ....
Address ....
....
....
....

Name ....
Tel ....
Address ....
....
....
....

Name ....
Tel ....
Address ....
....
....

Quotations for Special Occasions

"Lovers may be, and indeed, generally are enemies, but they can never be friends."

Bryon

"No one knows what he can do till he tries."

Publilius Syrus

"The chains of marriage are so heavy that it takes two to bear them, sometimes three."

Alexandre Dumas Fils

"The years between fifty and seventy are the hardest. You are always being asked to do things, and yet you are not decrepit enough to turn them down."

T. S. Eliot

"Tears may linger at nightfall, but joy comes in the morning."

Psalms 126:5

"The right man is the one who seizes the moment."

Johann Wolfgang von Goethe: Faust

"There is only one pretty child in the world, and every mother has it."

Chinese Proverb

"You are as welcome as the flowers in May."

Charles Macklin

"Life is long to the miserable, but short to the happy."

Publilius Syrus

M

Name ....
Tel ....
Address ....
....
....

Name ....
Tel ....
Address ....
....
....

Name ....
Tel ....
Address ....
....
....

M

Name ....
Tel ....
Address ....
....
....

Name ....
Tel ....
Address ....
....
....

Name ....
Tel ....
Address ....

Quotations for Special Occasions

"Success seems to be largely a
matter of hanging on after
others have let go."

William Feather

"Sadness flies on the wings of the
morning and out of the heart of
darkness comes the light."

Jean Giraudoux

"A cough is something that
you yourself can't help, but
everybody else does on purpose
just to torment you."

Ogden Nash

"Vincit qui se vincit."
*[He conquers who conquers
himself]*

Latin Proverb

"In travelling: a man must carry
knowledge with him, if he would
bring home knowledge."

Samuel Johnson

"All changes, even the most longed
for, have their melancholy; for
what we leave behind us is
a part of ourselves; we must die
to one other life before we can
enter into another!"

Anatole France

"There is no hope of joy except
in human relations."

Saint-Exupéry

"A smooth sea never made
a skilful mariner."

English Proverb

M-N

Name ....
Tel ....
Address ....
....
....

Name ....
Tel ....
Address ....
....
....
....

Name ....
Tel ....
Address ....
....
....

Name ....
Tel ....
Address ....
....
....

Name ....
Tel ....
Address ....
....
....
....

Name ....
Tel ....
Address ....
....
....

For the sunshine
and the rain.
For the dew and for
the shower.
or the yellow
ripened

Quotations for Special Occasions

"The joys of meeting pay
the pangs of absence;
Else who could bear it?"

Nicholas Rowe

"Winning is not a sometime thing;
it's an all-time thing. You don't
win once in a while, you don't do
things right once in a while,
you do them right all the time.
Winning is a habit.
Unfortunately, so is losing."

Vince Lombardi

"When you were born,
you cried and the world rejoiced.
Live your life in such a manner
that when you die the world
cries and you rejoice."

Old Indian Saying

"There never was child so lovely
but his mother was glad to
get him asleep."

Ralph Waldo Emerson

"A grateful mind, by owing
owes not, but still pays, at once
Indebted and discharged."

Milton: Paradise Lost

"If it were not for the presents, an
elopement would be preferable."

George Ade

"Grief can take care of itself,
but to get the full value of joy
you must have somebody to
divide it with."

Mark Twain

N

Name ....
Tel ....
Address ....
....
....
....

Name ....
Tel ....
Address ....
....
....
....

Name ....
Tel ....
Address ....
....
....
....

N

Name ....
Tel ....
Address ....
....
....
....

Name ....
Tel ....
Address ....
....
....
....

Name ....
Tel ....
Address ....
....
....

Quotations for Special Occasions

"It's not that age brings
childhood back again,
Age merely shows what
children we remain."

Johann Wolfgang von Goethe: Faust

"The love we give away is
the only love we keep."

Elbert Hubbard

"There's no vocabulary
For love within a family,
love that's lived in
But not looked at,
love within the light of which
All else is seen,
the love within which
All other love finds speech.
This love is silent."

T. S. Eliot

"He who limps is still walking."

Stanislaw Lec

"If you want to succeed in the
world you must make your
own opportunities."

John B. Gough

"If a man does not keep pace with
his companions, perhaps it is
because he hears a different
drummer. Let him step to the
music he hears, however
measured or far away."

Thoreau

"It is not the years in your life
but the life in your years
that counts!"

Adlai Stevenson

Quotations for Special Occasions

"No spring, nor summer beauty
hath such grace,
As I have seen in one
autumnal face."

John Donne

"Nothing is impossible to
a willing heart."

John Heywood

"Love is an act of endless
forgiveness, a tender look which
becomes a habit."

Peter Ustinov

"Change is the law of life.
And those who look only to the
past or the present are certain
to miss the future."

John F. Kennedy

"Gratefulness is the poor
man's payment."

English Proverb

"Grief is a tree that has tears
for its fruit."

Philemon

"Let there be spaces in your
togetherness."

Kahlil Gibran

"Experience is the name everyone
gives to their mistakes."

Oscar Wilde: Lady Windermere's Fan

"Learning without thought is
labour lost; thought without
learning is perilous."

Confucius

O

Name ....
Tel ....
Address ....
....
....
....

Name ....
Tel ....
Address ....
....
....

Name ....
Tel ....
Address ....
....
....

Name ....
Tel ....
Address ....
....
....
....

Name ....
Tel ....
Address ....
....
....

Name ....
Tel ....
Address ....
....

O

Name ....

Tel ....

Address ....

....

....

....

Name ....

Tel ....

Address ....

....

....

....

Name ....

Tel ....

Address ....

....

....

P

Name ....

Tel ....

Address ....

....

....

....

Name ....

Tel ....

Address ....

....

....

....

Name ....

Tel ....

Address ....

....

....

So Teach us
to Number our
Days, that we
may apply
our Heart
unto Wisdom.

Psalm xc.12.

Quotations for Special Occasions

"I keep my friends as misers
do their treasure, because, of all
the things granted us by wisdom,
none is greater or better
than friendship."

Pietro Aretino

"Content makes poor men rich;
discontent makes rich men poor."

Benjamin Franklin

"Courage is resistance to fear,
mastery of fear, not absence
of fear."

Mark Twain

"Thinking well is wise;
planning well, wiser;
doing well wisest and best of all."

Persian Proverb

"Monday's child is fair of face,
Tuesday's child is full of grace,
Wednesday's child is full of woe,
Thursday's child has far to go,
Friday's child is loving
and giving,
Saturday's child works hard
for a living,
But the child that's born
on the Sabbath day
Is bonny and blithe
and good and gay."

Anon

"The proper office of a friend
is to side with you when you are in
the wrong. Nearly anybody
will side with you when you
are in the right."

Mark Twain

P

Name ....
Tel ....
Address ....
....
....
....

Name ....
Tel ....
Address ....
....
....
....

Name ....
Tel ....
Address ....
....
....
....

Name ....
Tel ....
Address ....
....
....
....

Name ....
Tel ....
Address ....
....
....
....

Name ....
Tel ....
Address ....
....
....
....

Q

Name ....
Tel ....
Address ....
....
....
....

Name ....
Tel ....
Address ....
....
....
....

Name ....
Tel ....
Address ....
....
....

Q

Name ....
Tel ....
Address ....
....
....
....

Name ....
Tel ....
Address ....
....
....
....

Name ....
Tel ....
Address ....
....
....

Quotations for Special Occasions

"I am only one; but still I am one.
I cannot do everything, but still
I can do something; I will not
refuse to do something I can do."

Helen Keller

"Though seas and land
betwixt us both
Our faith and troth,
Like separated souls,
All time and space controls:
Above the highest sphere
we meet,
Unseen, unknown;
and greet as angels greet."

Richard Lovelace

"The harder you work the
luckier you get."

Gary Player

"He who does not hope to
win has already lost."

José Joaquin Olmedo

"I walk firmer and more secure
uphill than down."

Montaigne

"A sweet child is the sweetest
thing in nature."

Charles Lamb

"Good company and good
discourse are the very sinews
of virtue."

Izaak Walton

"Never, never, never,
never give up."

Sir Winston Churchill

Quotations for Special Occasions

"Blessed is he who expects
nothing, for he shall never be
disappointed."

Alexander Pope

"Love feeds on hope, they say,
or love will die – Ah miserie!
Yet my love lives, although no hope
have I! – Ah miserie."

W. S. Gilbert

"Any married man should forget
his mistakes – no use two people
remembering the same thing."

Duane Dewel

"Middle age is when your
age starts to show around
the middle."

Bob Hope

"The joys of parents are secret,
and so are their griefs and fears:
they cannot utter the one, nor they
will not utter the other."

Francis Bacon

"We only part to meet again."

John Gay

"Whenever a man's friends begin
to compliment him about looking
young, he may be sure that they
think he is growing old."

Washington Irving

"To know after absence the
familiar street and road and
village and house is to know again
the satisfaction of home."

Hal Borland

Quotations for Special Occasions

"Age is opportunity no less
Than youth itself,
though in another dress,
And as the evening twilight
fades away
The sky is filled with stars,
invisible by day."

Longfellow

"Well-married, a man is winged –
ill-matched, he is shackled."

Henry Ward Beecher

"To be able to enjoy one's past life
is to live twice."

Martial

"Few things are impossible to
diligence and skill."

Samuel Johnson

"Love, all alike, no season
knows, nor clime,
Nor hours, age, months,
which are the rags of time."

John Donne

"Wives are young men's
mistresses, companions for middle
age, and old men's nurses."

Francis Bacon

"No metaphysician ever felt
the deficiency of language so much
as the grateful."

Charles Caleb Colton

"A man's worth is no greater than
the worth of his ambitions."

Marcus Aurelius Antonnius

Q

Name ....

Tel ....

Address ....

....

....

....

Name ....

Tel ....

Address ....

....

....

....

Name ....

Tel ....

Address ....

....

....

R

Name ....

Tel ....

Address ....

....

....

....

Name ....

Tel ....

Address ....

....

....

....

Name ....

Tel ....

Address ....

....

....

R

Name ....
Tel ....
Address ....
....
....
....

Name ....
Tel ....
Address ....
....
....
....

Name ....
Tel ....
Address ....
....
....

R

Name ....
Tel ....
Address ....
....
....
....

Name ....
Tel ....
Address ....
....
....
....

Name ....
Tel ....
Address ....
....
....

Quotations for Special Occasions

"It's a funny thing about life; if you refuse to accept anything but the best, you very often get it."

Somerset Maugham

"A friend is a person with whom I may be sincere. Before him I may think aloud."

Ralph Waldo Emerson

"In matters of style, swim with the current; in matters of principle, stand like a rock."

Thomas Jefferson

"We have no more right to consume happiness without producing it than to consume wealth without producing it."

George Bernard Shaw: Candida

"Who takes the child by the hand, takes the mother by the heart."

Danish Proverb

"What matters is not the size of the dog in the fight, but the size of the fight in the dog."

Coach Bear Bryant

"There is more felicity on the far side of baldness than young men can possibly imagine."

Logan Pearsall Smith

"How great love is, presence best trial makes, But absence tries how long this love will be."

John Donne

Quotations for Special Occasions

"That which does not kill me
makes me stronger."

F. W. Nietzsche

"A friend is a gift you
give yourself."

Robert Louis Stevenson

"Life's aspirations come in the
guise of children."

Rabindranath Tagore

"Back of every achievement is
a proud wife and a surprised
mother-in-law."

Brooks Hays

"Give a man a fish and you
feed him for one day.
Teach a man to fish and you
feed him for a lifetime."

Chinese Proverb

"The most fortunate of men,
Be he a king or commoner, is he
Whose welfare is assured in
his own home."

Johann Wolfgang von Goethe

"The quality of a person's life is in
direct proportion to their
commitment to excellence,
regardless of their chosen field
of endeavour."

Vince Lombardi

"Treasure the love you receive
above all. It will survive long
after your gold and good health
have vanished."

Og Mandino

S-T

Name ....
Tel ....
Address ....
....
....
....

Name ....
Tel ....
Address ....
....
....
....

Name ....
Tel ....
Address ....
....
....
....

Name ....
Tel ....
Address ....
....
....
....

Name ....
Tel ....
Address ....
....
....
....

Name ....
Tel ....
Address ....
....
....
....

Quotations for Special Occasions

"Grow old along with me!
The best is yet to be,
The last of life, for which
the first was made:
Our times are in His hand
Who saith 'A whole I planned,
Youth shows but half; trust God:
see all nor be afraid!' "

Robert Browning

"A father is a banker by nature."

French Proverb

"One of the most difficult things to
contend with in a hospital is the
assumption on the part of the staff
that because you have lost
your gall bladder you have also
lost your mind."

Jean Kerr

"Our joys as winged
dreams do fly,
Why then should sorrow last?"

Thomas Percy

"Know how sublime a thing it is to
suffer and be strong."

Longfellow

"The less a tourist knows,
the fewer mistakes he need make,
for he will not expect himself to
explain ignorance."

Henry Adams

"I guess walking slow getting
married is because it gives
you time to maybe change
your mind."

Virginia Cary Hudson

Quotations for Special Occasions

"A man's home is
his wife's castle."

Alexander Chase

"A friend may well be reckoned
the masterpiece of nature."

Ralph Waldo Emerson

"Unable are the Loved to die
For Love is Immortality."

Emily Dickinson

"We never know the love of
our parents for us till we have
become parents."

Henry Ward Beecher

"By perseverance the snail
reached the Ark."

C. H. Spurgeon

"Old men like to give good advice
in order to console themselves
for not being any longer able
to set bad examples."

François de la Rochefoucauld

"We wasters of sorrows!
How we stare away into sad
endurance beyond them,
trying to foresee their end!
Whereas they are nothing else
than our winter foliage,
our sombre evergreen, one of the
seasons of our interior year."

Rainer Maria Rilke

"He has achieved success who has
lived well, laughed often
and loved much."

Bessie Anderson Stanley

T

Name	Name ....
Tel	Tel ....
Address	Address ....
....	....
....	....
....	....

Name	Name ....
Tel	Tel ....
Address	Address ....
....	....
....	....
....	....

Name	Name ....
Tel	Tel ....
Address	Address ....
....	....
....	....

U

Name ....
Tel ....
Address ....
....
....
....

Name ....
Tel ....
Address ....
....
....
....

Name ....
Tel ....
Address ....
....
....

U

Name ....
Tel ....
Address ....
....
....
....

Name ....
Tel ....
Address ....
....
....
....

Name ....
Tel ....
Address ....
....
....

U

Name ....
Tel ....
Address ....
....
....

Name ....
Tel ....
Address ....
....
....

Name ....
Tel ....
Address ....
....
....

V

Name ....
Tel ....
Address ....
....
....

Name ....
Tel ....
Address ....
....
....

Name ....
Tel ....
Address ....
....
....

Quotations for Special Occasions

"A traveller without knowledge
is a bird without wings."

Sa'di

"Holy is the wife; revered the
mother; galliptious is the
summer girl – but the bride is
the certified cheque among
the wedding presents that the
gods send in when man is
married to mortality."

O. Henry

"Youth does not require reasons
for living, it only needs pretexts."

José Ortega y Gasset

"Happiness makes up in height for
what it lacks in length."

Robert Frost

"They sicken of the calm,
who know the storm."

Dorothy Parker

"The only place where
success comes before work
is in a dictionary."

Vidal Sassoon

"In youth, we clothe ourselves
with rainbows, and go as brave
as the zodiac."

Ralph Waldo Emerson

"Education is an admirable
thing, but it is well to
remember from time to time
that nothing that is worth knowing
can be taught."

Oscar Wilde

Quotations for Special Occasions

"A Wounded Deer—
leaps highest."

Emily Dickinson

"What [Time] hath scanted
men in hair, he hath given
them in wit."

*William Shakespeare:
The Comedy of Errors*

"The secret of success is
constancy to purpose."

Benjamin Disraeli

"Life is a country that the
old have seen, and lived in.
Those who have to travel
through it can only learn the
way from them."

Joseph Joubert

"Marriage is popular because
it combines the maximum of
temptation with the
maximum of opportunity."

Shelley

"Gratitude is the most exquisite
form of courtesy."

Jacques Maritain

"One man with courage
is a majority."

Andrew Jackson

"Unto each man comes a day
when his favourite sins
all forsake him,
And he complacently thinks
he has forsaken his sins."

John Hay

V

Name ....
Tel ....
Address ....
....
....
....

Name ....
Tel ....
Address ....
....
....
....

Name ....
Tel ....
Address ....
....
....

For the sunsh...
and the ...
For the dew and ...
the s...
For the yellow ...
ripened grain,
And the golden
harvest hour,
We bless thee
O our God.

His
Compassions
fail not.
... ne ...

Quotations for Special Occasions

"Your friend is the man
who knows all about you
and still likes you."

Elbert Hubbard

"They can because they
think they can."
[Posunt, quia posse videntur]

Virgil

"Middle age is when you've
met so many people, that every
new person you meet reminds you
of someone else."

Ogden Nash

"The man who has never made
a fool of himself in love will
never be wise in love."

Theodor Reik

"The return makes one
love the farewell."

Alfred de Musset

"An adventure is only
an inconvenience rightly
considered. An inconvenience
is only an adventure
wrongly considered."

G. K. Chesterton

"You are a king by your own
fire-side, as much as any
monarch in his throne."

Cervantes

"There is no failure except in
no longer trying."

Elbert Hubbard

Quotations for Special Occasions

"The greater the difficulty,
the more glory in surmounting."

Epicurus

"In heaven above,
And earth below, they best
can serve true gladness
Who meet most feelingly
the calls of sadness."

William Wordsworth

"A man's wife has more power over
him that the state has."

Ralph Waldo Emerson

"Nothing flatters a man as much
as the happiness of his wife;
he is always proud of himself
as the source of it."

Samuel Johnson

"It is wrong to sorrow
without ceasing."

Homer

"The toughest thing about success
is that you've got to
keep on being a success."

Irving Berlin

"Marriage, n. the state or
condition of a community
consisting of a master,
a mistress, and two slaves,
making, in all, two."

Ambrose Bierce

"Married couples who love each
other tell each other a thousand
things without talking."

Chinese Proverb

W

Name ....
Tel ....
Address ....
....
....
....

Name ....
Tel ....
Address ....
....
....
....

Name ....
Tel ....
Address ....
....
....
....

Name ....
Tel ....
Address ....
....
....
....

Name ....
Tel ....
Address ....
....
....
....

Name ....
Tel ....
Address ....
....
....
....

W-X-Y-Z

Name ....
Tel ....
Address ....
....
....
....

Name ....
Tel ....
Address ....
....
....
....

Name ....
Tel ....
Address ....
....
....
....

Name ....
Tel ....
Address ....
....
....
....

Name ....
Tel ....
Address ....
....
....
....

Quotations for Special Occasions

"Bride, n. A woman with a fine prospect of happiness behind her."

Ambrose Bierce

"The ornament of a house is the friends who frequent it."

Ralph Waldo Emerson

"To have a friend, be a friend."

English Proverb

"Difficulties strengthen the mind, as labour does the body."

Seneca

"One of the best hearing aids a man can have is an attentive wife."

Groucho Marx

"God will not look you over for medals, degrees or diplomas, but for scars."

Elbert Hubbard

"The heaviest baggage for a traveller is an empty purse."

English Proverb

"The aim of education should be to convert the mind into a living fountain, and not a reservoir."

John M. Mason

"He who would travel happily must travel light."

Saint-Exupéry

"Children are poor men's riches."

English Proverb

Quotations for Special Occasions

"Children are the true connoisseurs. What's precious to them has no price, only value."

Bel Kaufman

"An old man loved is winter with flowers."

German Proverb

"Often the difference between a successful marriage and a mediocre one consists of leaving about three or four things a day unsaid."

Harlan Miller

"Old age is a tyrant who forbids, upon pain of death, all the pleasures of youth."

François de la Rochefoucauld

"Who, being loved, is poor?"

Oscar Wilde

"When the One Great Scorer comes to write against your name, He marks, not that you won or lost, but how you played the game."

Grantland Rice

"Man is that he might have joy."

Joseph Smith

"We are healed of a suffering only by experiencing it to the full."

Marcel Proust

"We are all born for love; it is the principle of existence and its only end."

Benjamin Disraeli

Misc

Name ....
Tel ....
Address ....
....
Name ....
....

Name ....
Tel ....
Address ....
....

Name ....
Tel ....
Address ....
....

To one I love

Sincerity